A Great Night!

30130505432665

Picture words

Twilight
Sparkle

Rainbow
Dash

Pinkie
Pie

Rarity

Applejack

Fluttershy

the prince

Princess
Celestia

Spike

the Wonderbolts

magic

forest

apple pie

carriage

sculpture

pillar

It was the night of the Pony Party, and the ponies were very excited.

"We are going to the Pony Party!" said Twilight Sparkle. "My magic can help us to get there."

Then, Twilight changed an apple into a beautiful carriage and horses!

"WOW!" said the ponies.
"What a beautiful carriage!"

Spike drove the ponies to the party.

"Thanks, Spike," said the ponies.
They were all very happy.
"This is a great night!" said
Twilight Sparkle.

"What do you want to do at the Pony Party, Fluttershy?" asked Twilight.

"I want to meet all the little animals," said Fluttershy.

"I want to sell all my apple pies and cakes," said Applejack.

"I want to meet a prince at the Pony Party," said Rarity.

"I want to fly with the Wonderbolts," said Rainbow Dash.

"I want to dance and have fun at the Pony Party," said Pinkie Pie.

"And I want to speak to Princess Celestia," said Twilight.

"There you are, Twilight!" said Princess Celestia. "You must stay near me all night. I want to talk to you about many things."

Twilight felt very happy.

"Look!" said Rarity to her friends. "There is a prince at the Pony Party!"

Rarity felt very happy.

"Look at that beautiful bird!" Fluttershy thought. "There are more little birds and animals in this forest. I must find them!"

Applejack was very happy
because she sold one of her pies.

"All the ponies want my apple
pies!" she thought.

"Do you want to be our friend?"
said one of the Wonderbolts
to Rainbow Dash.

"Yes, please!" said Rainbow Dash.

"Look at the beautiful dance floor!" said Pinkie Pie.

She ran to the dance floor, and began to sing and dance.

Fluttershy went into the forest.

"Hello, little animals," she said.
But all the little animals ran
from her.

There were many ponies who wanted to say hello to Princess Celestia.

"Good evening!" said Princess Celestia.

"The princess has no time to speak to me," Twilight thought, sadly.

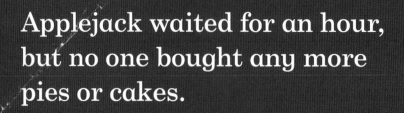

Applejack waited for an hour, but no one bought any more pies or cakes.

"No one wants to eat my pies or cakes, because there is other food at the Pony Party," said Applejack. She felt very sad.

Rarity was with the prince in the garden. He put a red flower in his hair.

"It looks nice on me," he said.

Rarity felt angry. She wanted the prince to give HER the flower!

Rainbow Dash was with the Wonderbolts, but they talked very loudly, and they could not hear her.

And no one wanted to dance
or have fun with Pinkie Pie
on the dance floor.

All the ponies were very angry.
The Pony Party was not a great
night for them!

"But we can try again!" they said.

So Applejack made a big, new
apple cake to sell at the party.

Pinkie Pie did a big jump on to the dance floor, but she hit the cake and it flew up.

The cake hit Rarity and
the prince!

The sculpture began to fall.
Rainbow Dash flew to help—but
she couldn't catch it.

The sculpture hit the pillars,
and they fell with it!

Then, lots of frightened little animals ran through the door, with Fluttershy behind them!

"Stop!" she shouted. "I want to talk to you!"

"Quickly, ponies! It's time for you to go," said Princess Celestia.

"Come on!" said Twilight, and the ponies all ran from the party. They felt very sad.

The ponies found Spike in a cake shop.

"How was your great night?" he asked them.

"It was terrible!" the ponies said.

"Do you think Princess Celestia is angry with us?" said Twilight.

Princess Celestia came into the cake shop. "No, I'm not angry with you!" she said. Then, she laughed.

"The Pony Party is always boring," she said. "I asked you to come because I wanted you to make it interesting! And you did!"

Activities

The key below describes the skills practiced in each activity.

Spelling and writing

Reading

Speaking

Critical thinking

Preparation for the Cambridge Young Learners Exams

1 Look at the pictures. Put a ✓ or a ✗ in the correct boxes. 📖

1

a Princess Celestia ✓
b the prince ☐

2

a Rarity ☐
b Twilight Sparkle ☐

3

a Pinkie Pie ☐
b Spike ☐

4

a Applejack ☐
b apple pie ☐

5

a Fluttershy ☐
b forest ☐

6

a little animals ☐
b Wonderbolts ☐

2 Look at the pictures. Match the two parts of the words, and write them on the lines.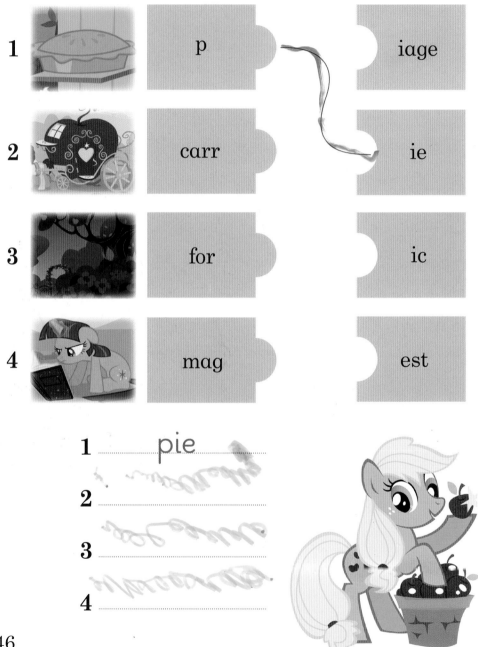

1 | p | iage

2 | carr | ie

3 | for | ic

4 | mag | est

1 pie

2 ....

3 ....

4 ....

3 Find the words. 📖

m	a	g	i	c	l	c	y	i	m
a	g	f	q	e	j	a	t	k	a
p	p	i	l	l	a	r	h	e	g
f	s	u	g	a	e	r	s	t	o
o	e	g	s	c	u	i	p	l	p
r	o	f	o	r	r	a	i	j	o
e	r	l	o	v	e	g	c	s	n
s	e	s	t	o	y	e	l	o	i
t	t	j	w	b	f	n	t	n	e
s	c	u	l	p	t	u	r	e	s

magic   carriage   forest

sculpture   pillar   ponies

4 Look at the letters. Write the words. 📖 ✏️ ⭐

1 (g a c m i)

"My ___magic___ can help us get there."

2 (g a r i c r e a)

She changed the apple into a
_____ and horses!

3 (r i n p e c)

"I want to meet a _____
at the Pony Party," said Rarity.

4 (c a n d e)

"I want to _____ and
have fun at the Pony Party,"
said Pinkie Pie.

5 Who said this?

Applejack   Rarity   Rainbow Dash   Fluttershy

1 "I want to meet all the little animals," said ___Fluttershy___ .

2 "I want to sell all my apple pies and cakes," said _____.

3 "I want to meet a prince at the Pony Party," said _____.

4 "I want to fly with the Wonderbolts," said _____.

6 **Read the questions.**
Write complete answers.

1 Who helped the ponies go
to the party?

Twilight helped the ponies
go to the party.

2 How did they get to the party?

_____

_____

3 How did the ponies feel about
the party?

_____

_____

7 Read and write *Rarity*, *Pinkie Pie*, *Applejack*, or *Twilight*. 📖 ✏️

1 ___Twilight___ changes an apple into a carriage and horses.

2 _____ wants to sell apple pies and cakes at the party.

3 _____ wants to dance and have fun.

4 _____ wants to meet a prince.

5 _____ wants to speak to Princess Celestia.

8 Look and read. Put a ✓ or a ✗ in the boxes. 📖 ✿

1 The apple changes into a beautiful carriage. ✓

2 The prince drives the ponies to the party. ☐

3 Twilight wants to talk to Princess Celestia. ☐

4 Rarity sees a prince at the Pony Party. ☐

5 Applejack sells three pies. ☐

9 **Read the text. Choose the correct words and write them next to 1—5.**

to dance	to fly	to go	to meet	to sell

All the ponies wanted ¹ **to go** to the Pony Party. Fluttershy wanted ² _____ all the little animals.

Applejack wanted ³ _____ all her apple pies and cakes. Rainbow Dash wanted ⁴ _____ with the Wonderbolts. Pinkie Pie wanted ⁵ _____ and have fun at the Pony Party.

10 Look at the pictures. Look at the letters and complete the words.

r p p r e f s i e a f m c t p a

1

m agi c

2

.... ores........

3

.... pple p........

4

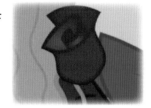

.... low........

5

.... ill........

6

.... onie........

54

11 Work with a friend. You are the ponies. Ask and answer questions about what you want to do at the party.

1

> Fluttershy, what do you want to do at the party?

> I want to meet all the little animals.

2

3

4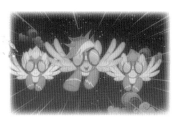

5

12 **Read the text. Choose the best answers.** ⬡ 📖

1 "There you are, Twilight!" said Princess Celestia. "You must _____ near me all night."

   (**a** stay)   **b** to stay

2 Pinkie Pie ran to the dance floor, and began _____ and dance.

   a sing   **b** to sing

3 "Oh no! The princess has no time to speak _____," Twilight thought sadly.

   a me   **b** to me

13 Write the correct sentences. 📖 ✏️

1 (beautiful) (What) (carriage) (a) (!)

What a beautiful carriage!

2 (drove) (party) (to) (the) (Spike)
(ponies) (the) (.)

3 (dance) (ran) (the) (to) (floor) (Pinkie Pie) (.)

4 (prince) (The) (a) (put) (in)
(his) (flower) (hair) (red) (.)

14 Write *and, because,* or *but.*

1 All the ponies were very angry
  because the Pony Party was not
  a great night for them!

2 No one bought any more pies or
  cakes, _____ there was
  other food at the party.

3 The Wonderbolts talked very loudly,
  _____ they could not
  hear Rainbow Dash.

4 Pinkie Pie ran to the dance floor,
  _____ no one wanted
  to dance or have fun with her.

5 Pinkie Pie did a big jump on to
  the dance floor, _____
  she hit the cake and it flew up.

Circle the correct words.

1  The **apple** / (**cake**) hit Rarity and the prince!

2  Rainbow Dash couldn't catch the **pillars.** / **sculpture.**

3  Lots of frightened little **animals** / **ponies** ran through the door.

4  The ponies all ran from the **forest.** / **party.**

5  "I asked you to come because I wanted you to make it **interesting!"** / **boring!"**

16 Work with a friend. Talk about the characters in the story. Use the words in the box. 🗨

apple pies	prince
Princess Celestia	dance and have fun
little animals	magic
the Wonderbolts	drive carriage

This is Twilight Sparkle. She does magic.

17 **Circle the correct pictures.**

1 How do the ponies get to the party?

a

b

2 Which falls first?

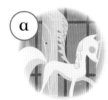
a

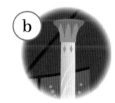
b

3 Where is the party?

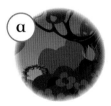
a

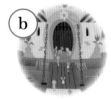
b

4 Who feels angry?

a

b

18 **Order the sentences.**
Write 1—5.

.... The sculpture hit the pillars, and they fell with it!

.... The cake hit Rarity and the prince.

.... Princess Celestia told the ponies to leave the party.

.... Pinkie Pie hit the cake, and it flew up.

....1.... Applejack made a big, new apple cake for the party.

19 Work with a friend. Ask and answer questions about parties.

1

> Do you like going to parties?

> Yes, I love going to parties!

2 What do you do at parties?

3 What do you wear to parties?

4 What do you take to parties?

Level 3

Sharks

978–0–241–25382–3 ☐

The Jungle Book

978–0–241–25383–0 ☐

The Red Knight

978–0–241–25384–7 ☐

The Elves and the Shoemaker

978–0–241–25385–4 ☐

Rapunzel

978–0–241–28394–3 ☐

Great Buildings

978–0–241–28400–1 ☐

Minibeasts

978–0–241–28404–9 ☐

Puss in Boots

978–0–241–28407–0 ☐

Jack and the Beanstalk

978–0–241–28397–4 ☐

Hansel and Gretel

978-0-241-29861-9 ☐

The Talent Show

978-0-241-29859-6 ☐

A Great Night!

978-0-241-29863-3 ☐

Bumblebee and the Rock Concert

978-0-241-29867-1 ☐

Where Animals Live

978-0-241-29868-8 ☐

Now you're ready for Level 4!